English Functional Skills

Levels 1 & 2

By Janet Marsh

INTRODUCTION

This resource is divided into 3 sections:-

- **LEARNING**
- **THE WORLD OF WORK**
- **LIFE**

Each section gives students practice in the components of Functional Skills assessed at levels 1-2 which are:-

- **READING**
- **WRITING**
- **SPEAKING AND LISTENING**

These skills are vital to all learners in many areas of life and they are assessed in slightly different ways by the examining boards.

READING AND WRITING are assessed in exams that are set and marked externally.

SPEAKING AND LISTENING are assessed under controlled conditions in school or college.

Every effort is made to ensure that the information provided in this publication is accurate. It is the policy of Coleridge Press to obtain permission on any copyright material in their publications. The publishers will be glad to make suitable arrangements with any copyright holders whom it has not been possible to contact.

Purchasers may photocopy the sheets in this pack provided that they do so only for use within their own institution.

ISBN 978-0-957493-51-3

Text by: Janet Marsh
Design and Layout by: David Jones

Published by Coleridge Press

Contents

Section 1 – Learning

Section 2 – World of Work

Section 3 – Life
Where to Live

Leisure Time

Shopping

Technology

SECTION 1: Learning

Reading

There are different types of reading that we do in our daily lives.
When in a hurry we:-

SKIM   Which means reading over the surface of the text to select the details we
want. We don't read every word, just get the main points. To help us pick out
the main points we can look at:-

- o Any section in bold.
- o Any subheading or bulleted point.
- o The first sentence of each paragraph which should sum up what the
    paragraph is going to be about.
- o Any keyword that we may be searching for to find the information we are
    reading - for example, *sixth form*.

SCAN   to pick out information. It means reading very quickly having an eye out for
key information.

**Skim and scan the web article on page 3 about education and training after 16 and answer
these questions:-**

1. Which 4 places could you continue
   your education after 16?
2. What is the term used to mean
   education after 16?
3. What are *vocational qualifications*?
4. According to the article, what subjects
   do learners usually do better at?
5. When should you apply for popular
   courses in college?
6. Where could you find yourself
   studying with adults?
7. Why does the article use
   subheadings?
8. Who is this article written for? How do
   you know?

Learning at college or sixth form

If you want to stay on in full-time education after 16, there are lots of courses to choose from. First you'll need to decide which subjects you want to focus on: you can then find a place to study. There are lots of resources online to help you.

What do you want to study?
To get the most out of studying after the age of 16 (sometimes known as 'further education'), it's important to take time to choose the right courses and qualifications.

Ask yourself:-

- what you are good at, and what you enjoy - most people do better when they study a subject they like.
- whether you want to learn something new - for many courses, you may not need any previous experience.
- what course structure will suit you - do you prefer end-of-year exams, continual assessment, or a mixture of both?
- what learning style will suit you - do you prefer lectures, classroom discussions, or practical workshops?

Qualifications: what's on offer?
You could study for academic qualifications such as AS or A levels, or go for work-related qualifications such as the new vocational qualifications on the Qualifications and Credit Framework. Selected colleges also offer the Diploma qualification for 14 to 19 year-olds.
You also need to think about how your choices of what to study will fit in with your career plans.

Choosing where to study
Once you've thought about what you're going to study, it's worth also considering which type of learning environment would suit you best. You could choose from:-

- a school sixth form
- a sixth form college
- a further education college
- a specialist college

Each type of institution has its own structure and atmosphere, and will offer a different range of subjects and courses.

Sixth forms
You may be able to study at your own school's sixth form, the sixth form of another school, or at a sixth form college. They offer a wider range of options than you've probably had to date, and the environment is usually more relaxed than in Year 11.
Sixth forms vary a lot in size, and in the courses and facilities they offer. Sixth form colleges tend to be larger and more informal than school sixth forms.

Further education colleges
Further education colleges can offer similar courses to sixth form colleges. They also vary a lot in size, and in the subjects and facilities they offer.

Your fellow students may include adults of all ages as well as young people.

You should start applying for popular or specialist courses in the autumn term of Year 11. For other courses, you normally apply in the spring.

You do not normally need to apply if you want to stay on at your school's own sixth form.

CLOSE READING implies you are reading more slowly with an eye on the **DETAIL** of the text. When you do this you are picking up on not just the facts but the **IDEAS** and **OPINIONS** in the text.

Home pupils to learn via Net at 'virtual school'

The first government-funded "virtual school", with lessons streamed via the internet to pupils at home, could open next year.

Up to 450 students could join the secondary, which would be based in Ealing, Slough or Windsor. It would be a free school and would take children who are currently educated at home.

If Education Secretary Michael Gove approves the business plan it could open in September 2012. John Edwards, principal of Periplus Home Education, which would run the school, said: "There are 80,000 home-educated students with no government support. Parents do a fantastic job but many pay for education online or tutors."

Teachers, hired in the same way as at mainstream schools, would deliver lessons from a main building. Students would be able to see them, but teachers would not see the children and classmates would not see each other.

Pupils would need a computer and broadband connection, but everything else would be provided by the school. An adult would have to be in the house while lessons are in progress.

1. Using information from the article, what are the advantages of this *virtual school*?
2. Why do you think *an adult* would have to be in the house while lessons were in progress?

Speaking and Listening

Imagine a discussion about what to do after 16 that takes place among a group of friends.

Ameera
wants to stay on at school and do "A" levels and eventually apply for university.

Kyle
hasn't done well at academic subjects at school and wants to train for a more practical future.

Lisa
cares part-time for her disabled mother but wants to continue her education and to improve her IT skills.

1. Discuss in groups which kind of further education would suit each of them and why.
2. Now take on the role of one of these characters and ROLE PLAY a discussion they might have among themselves.

Reading

Financial support for post 16 students

Students who are staying on in education, studying an eligible course, and who live in a household with an annual income of £30,000 or less can apply for an EMA.

Pupils from low-income families who wish to remain in school beyond the statutory school leaving age may be able to claim the Welsh Assembly Government's Education Maintenance Allowance.

The EMA Wales website provides help and information for:

- Students
- Parents and guardians
- Learning Centres

1. What is meant by the statutory school leaving age? What is it?
2. What does EMA stand for?
3. Would having financial support to stay on in school persuade you to stay on? Give your reasons.

Writing

Fill in this section of an application form for a FE college.

APPLICATION FORM

Thank you for your interest in Swinburn College.
If you need any help completing this application form, contact Student Services on 01254 292929.

Name of School _____

ABOUT YOURSELF

Surname _____   First Name _____

Gender _____   Date of Birth _____

Home Address _____

_____

Postcode _____   Phone Number _____

Email address _____   Mobile Number _____

Have you been a permanent resident in the UK for the last three years? *(please circle)*   YES/NO

If no, please specify country: _____   Nationality _____

Name of Emergency Contact _____   Phone Number _____

The form is much more detailed than this but at the end, you would find this:

Data Protection

The information you provide on this application form will be stored and used by the College, which is registered under the Data Protection Act 1998, for the primary reason of monitoring the progress of your application. The data may be shared with your school, Connexions and the LSC. Swinburn College may use this data to contact you in the future.

Tick this box if you like to opt out. ☐

---

1.   What does *tick this box if you want to opt out* mean?
2.   Look at what is written under the heading Data Protection. In your own words, what does it mean?

Reading

Schools and colleges have to compete for students and sell themselves to attract the best students. To do this, they produce brochures, prospectuses and create attractive websites.

Use the Internet to look at the following:-

- Gloucester Sixth Form College
- Brookland College, Surrey
- Burton and South Derbyshire College

Now use the following questions to rate each website using **1 to 5** ☆ :-

- ✓ Does the college have a logo?
- ✓ Is it easy to find information about FE courses?
- ✓ Does the site give you information about the college's:-
  - success
  - facilities
  - requirements for entry
- ✓ Does it tell you about how social life you could have there?
- ✓ Does it talk about:-
  - sports facilities
  - food
  - how to get there
- ✓ Does it give you testimonials from other students *in their own words?*
- ✓ Does it use images/photographs to draw you in?
- ✓ Does it tell you how to apply?

The following basic information is about a fictional college, **BRINKWORTH FE COLLEGE**.

LOCATION	3 MILES OUTSIDE THE CITY OF BRABY	
BUILDINGS	BUILT IN 2001- EXCELLENT FACILITIES	
COURSES	A/AS LEVELS	*DRAMA ENGLISH SOCIOLOGY MEDIA STUDIES ECONOMICS MUSIC TECHNOLOGY*
	FUNCTIONAL SKILLS	*MATHS ENGLISH IT*
	VOCATIONAL COURSES	*HAIRDRESSING BEAUTY THERAPY*
APPRENTICESHIPS	PLUMBING HEATING ENGINEERING	
CLUBS AND SOCIETIES	DRAMA CLUB FILM CLUB FOOTBALL TENNIS	
FACILITIES	SPORTS FIELDS THEATRE MUSIC STUDIO	
DURATION OF COURSES	1- 4 YEARS	

Writing

Now working in groups decide how to promote this college to young people by producing an A5 brochure.

> **REMEMBER!**
>
> Don't just list the facts but make them want to study there. Use language that will PERSUADE as well as INFORM.

To do this you could use:-

✓ Questions
   e.g. *Are you ambitious?*
✓ Command / imperative
   e.g. *Come to our open day and see for yourself.*
✓ Tripling
   e.g. It's *a college that offers a wide range of courses, is friendly and close to the town.*

Use graphics, images, a logo. Think carefully about the layout. Include student quotes if you like.

You can do this project using IT if you like.

You have just applied for a place at this college. Write to a friend who lives abroad and tell him/her about the college and your plans to study there.

This is an informal letter so remember:-

✓ Correct layout
✓ Informal tone
✓ Include some other news

| Paragraph 1 |
| Paragraph 2 |
| Paragraph 3 |

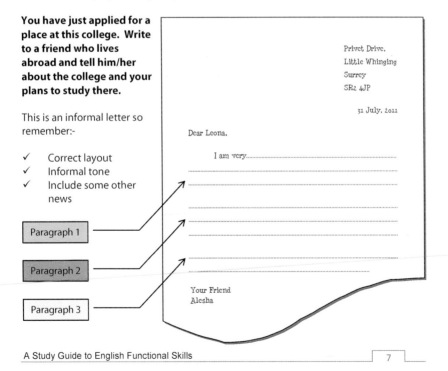

Privet Drive,
Little Whinging
Surrey
SR2 4JP

31 July, 2011

Dear Leona,

I am very...

....

....

....

....

....

....

....

Your Friend
Alesha

Writing

Your school / college is organizing a day trip to London by coach to visit the Houses of Parliament and the Tower of London. The cost will be twenty pounds which covers entry fees but does not include food as pupils are expected to bring a packed lunch.

The coach will leave from school at 8 am and is expected to return about 8 pm.

Write a letter to parents / guardians from the staff trip organizer:

- setting out the facts.
- making the trip sound worthwhile and fun.

Reading

After you have finished in school, you may want to continue learning at college. Will you stay in your home town or move away?

Planning School Trips Abroad? Get Unbeatable Online Quote!

Europe for Schools is a school travel company specialising in school trips, study tours and educational visits abroad.

Our expertise is in arranging school trips and educational tours that offer a stress free and memorable experience.
We provide complete peace of mind by organising educational travel that is designed to suit your requirements of destination, duration, visits and cost.

Pick out the details of this advertisement that will appeal to teachers organizing a trip and give your reasons.

Read the article over the page and answer the questions on it.

Should you stay or go?

Is it better to find a university or college near your family home or get a fresh start in a new environment? Here are some points to consider.

For most students going to university or college in the UK used to mean leaving home. Thousands of people do still move away to study. But with so many places to study and so many courses on offer, many people now opt to stay at home and study close to where they live. The choice is yours!

Why live at home?

Living at home while studying in Higher Education (HE) has been the norm in countries such as France and Australia for a long time. By staying put, you can often save money on rent and keep in touch with home life – while still making new friends and having new experiences. For some people it offers 'the best of both worlds', and it is becoming more popular. Expansion in HE means that it is more likely that the right course for you could be close to home. If it's within commuting distance, then staying put is worth some serious thought.

The Pros:-

- ✓ It's often cheaper than renting or moving into student accommodation.
- ✓ You avoid the hassle of moving and travelling to get home.
- ✓ Makes it easier to keep close to family and friends.
- ✓ Provides home comforts and stability.
- ✓ Offers the 'best of both worlds'.

The Cons:-

- ✗ It can restrict your choice of course.
- ✗ You may have less independence.
- ✗ Other friends may move away to study.

Why move away?

For some, getting away from home is reason enough to go to university – sometimes the further away the better! In the UK it used to be the norm that most students went to live on or near campus, and there is still a strong tradition of moving away to study for a degree. In some cases, the preferred course may be at a specific university or college, in which case it may make good sense to move. Some students also value the experience of living in student halls of residence, or in shared accommodation, as an important part of university life. Others want the opportunity to experience living in a different part of the country.

The Pros:-

- ✓ Gives you more independence.
- ✓ Allows you to discover a different part of the country.
- ✓ Brings you close to campus.
- ✓ Gives you greater choice of courses.
- ✓ Gives you the chance to live with other students.

The Cons:-

- ✗ You will be further away from home and family.
- ✗ It may be more expensive.
- ✗ You may have to live with other students!

'Should I stay or should I go?' is a decision that very much depends on your personality and the kind of experience you want from university.

1. What is HE short for?
2. What does *commuting distance* mean?
3. What do the PROS and CONS mean?
4. What does it *used to be the norm* mean?
5. What is a *university campus*?
6. How might the way this article is set out help you come to decision if you were unsure about staying or leaving?

Writing

Your friend has decided to move a hundred miles away to take a college course next September. He/she could do the same course in your home town and you think that going away is not the best choice.

Write an email saying why you think he/she ought to stay.

Getting It Right

A common mistake in writing is to mix the tenses you use **e.g.**

✗   *When I was in the stadium, I see the Scarlets beaten by the Blues.*
✗   *I go down to the shops every Saturday with Mum and we bought some doughnuts home for tea.*

The TENSE of a verb tell you when an action takes place. The most common confusion is between PAST and PRESENT tenses.

There are three main tenses we use in English:

PRESENT

This means that what is happening is going on NOW or happens REGULARLY **e.g.**

✓   *Every week Kyle **goes** over to Jamal's after football practice.*
    OR
✓   *"She's **running** the best race of her life!" **screams** Laura as she **sees** her sister thunder past the winning post.*

PAST

This means the action has already happened.

✓   *He **lived** in the USA for seven years.*
✓   Before she **left** the house, she **locked** the door.
✓   She **had** never really **wanted** a puppy but her father **bought** her one for her birthday.

REMEMBER!

There is often more than one part to a verb **e.g.** *had wanted*
The usual rule to turn an English verb into the past tense is to add 'ed' **e.g.**

walk - ed   pack - ed   march - ed   return - ed

However there are many verbs that are exceptions to this rule.

Look at the following list and fill in the PAST TENSES of these PRESENT TENSE verbs.

PRESENT TENSE	PAST TENSE	PRESENT TENSE	PAST TENSE
RUN		READ	
SWIM		DRINK	
SEE		SEND	
AM		SPEND	
KNOW		DIG	
EAT		HAVE	
DRIVE		DO	
DRAW		TAKE	
LEAD		LOSE	
HIT		KEEP	
LIGHT		FIGHT	

REMEMBER!
the past tense of **I SEE** is **I SAW - not I SEEN** (though you can say
I HAVE SEEN).

Now correct the tenses/verbs in the following piece of writing.

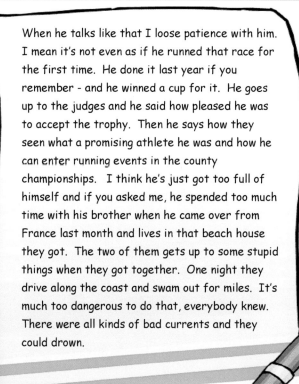

When he talks like that I loose patience with him. I mean it's not even as if he runned that race for the first time. He done it last year if you remember - and he winned a cup for it. He goes up to the judges and he said how pleased he was to accept the trophy. Then he says how they seen what a promising athlete he was and how he can enter running events in the county championships. I think he's just got too full of himself and if you asked me, he spended too much time with his brother when he came over from France last month and lives in that beach house they got. The two of them gets up to some stupid things when they got together. One night they drive along the coast and swam out for miles. It's much too dangerous to do that, everybody knew. There were all kinds of bad currents and they could drown.

The third tense we commonly use is the:

FUTURE

This tells us when things are going to happen **e.g.**

- ✓ *Ryan **will be** staying with you for three days.*
- ✓ *She**'ll** be entering her cake for the competition.*

Notice that *will* or *shall* is often shortened to'll in less formal English.

We only use the *shall* form of the future tense when using **I** or **we e.g.**

- ✓ *I shall be ready to leave at half past six.*
- ✓ **We** *shall look forward to your visit.*

SECTION 2: The World of Work

Reading

Read the following 3 job descriptions then answer the questions that follow.

NURSERY NURSE

Your Job Education are looking for qualified Nursery Nurses to start work immediately! They will be expected to contribute to a programme of activities for the children in their care. They will be responsible for the children's well being, safety and physical care.

Typical work activities include:-
- Helping children with their learning, play, educational and social development.
- Feeding, washing and cleaning young children.
- Record keeping.
- Supporting workers in community settings.
- Making and maintaining learning materials and resources.

We are looking to recruit people who are passionate about working with young people. The ideal candidates will have previous experience of working with children.

If you are flexible, enthusiastic and committed, then we have the right work for you. Each candidate will need to have an enhanced Criminal records disclosure which we can help you obtain.

If you are interested please email your CV and covering letter to:-
office@yourjobeducation.com

1. Why might *record keeping* be useful for the job?
2. Do you need formal qualifications for this job?
3. When will you start if you get the job?
4. What do you think *making and maintaining learning materials and resources* means?
5. What is meant by an *enhanced Criminal records disclosure*?

TEACHING ASSISTANT

Your Job Education are looking for a Teaching Assistant for a Reception Class in a Primary school fifteen miles from the city centre. It is a temporary one year, full - time vacancy to commence in September 2011.

The successful candidate will be required to work under the instruction of teaching / senior staff in the Reception Classroom to support the teacher in the management of pupils and the classroom, including preparation and routine maintenance of resources / equipment. Each candidate will need to have an enhanced Criminal records disclosure which we can help you obtain.

- **Date Posted:** *2nd Sep 2010*
- **Salary:** *£6.79 p/h*
- **Location:** Eastley
- **Reference Code:** *BR107295*
- **Views Since Posting:** *573*

1. Where will the job be?
2. When does it start?
3. What extra information does this advertisement give you which 1 didn't?
4. How might this information help you decide whether to apply for the job or not?
5. Is this job suitable for someone looking for a permanent job?

RECEPTIONIST

Salary: £6.75ph. Our client is seeking a receptionist to work in a busy medical practice based just outside the city centre. They are looking for the successful candidate to be confident when liaising with patients, have a positive attitude and be flexible and friendly.

Job Responsibilities:-

- Greeting patients
- Dealing with inbound and outbound calls
- Typing up Doctors Notes
- Basic administration duties

Preferred Skills:-

- Previous experience working within a medical organisation
- Previous experience of using a system called (Vision) or (EMIS - Pcs)

Personal Attributes:

- Highly organised and able to prioritise workloads
- Good verbal and written communication skills

Normal working week is between 16 - 30 hours through Monday - Friday.

1. How much would you expect to earn in this job if you worked a 30 hour week?
2. How will you apply for this job?
3. What does *good transport links* mean?
4. What does *confident when liaising with patients* mean?
5. What does *prioritising workloads* mean?
6. How do we know that this advertisement was placed by an AGENCY?

Speaking and Listening

Now think about this:

Louise has 4 GCSEs grade C and above. She has no typing skills, she has her own car. She is seventeen, quiet and shy but very hard working and dependable. She thinks that she might go to college next year and get some more qualifications and maybe train to be a chef. She is very good at making things - clothes, gifts, and toys.

Discuss with a partner the following:-

1. Which of these 3 jobs would suit her and explain your reasons fully. Maybe none of these will be ideal for her.

2. What sort of job would suit her?
    Look at 3 jobsites and find 3 jobs she can apply for.

jobsite.co.uk is part of our local family

Reading and Writing

APPLYING FOR JOBS

Most jobs must be applied for by filling in a **form**, possibly **online**, but if you send it by post, you will have to send a short **covering letter** with it too.

Imagine that you are applying for one of the following three jobs and have filled in an application form. **Write a covering letter to go with the application form.**

PERSONAL TRAINER

- Are you passionate about Sport, Health and Fitness?
  Then a career in Personal Training could be for you.
- If you're longing to launch yourself into an exciting and rewarding career doing something you love, and possess the drive and determination to be the very best, then The Training Room could be just the answer.
- As the UK's leading Personal Trainer Academy, we are now recruiting for 2010/2011 intakes and invite applications from highly motivated individuals with a proven track record for success. We offer some of the UK's leading training facilities, distraction free learning and the opportunity to work and train alongside the very best. We are also the chosen provider of employees to the UK's leading leisure companies such as David Lloyd Health Clubs, Virgin Active, Esporta Health Clubs, Greens Health Clubs, LA Fitness PT, Harding Brothers Spa Division (Cruise Ships) and Mark Warner Holidays (overseas placements).
- If successful, you will be offered an exclusive place on our Fast Track training scheme where you'll gain nationally recognised qualifications in Personal Training (REPS 3), Exercise to Music, Spinning, Circuit Training and Sports Nutrition. You'll also enjoy professional development and mentoring from our experienced tutors and personal trainers so you can enter the industry with all the qualifications and experience required to win the right job for you.
- During training we will guarantee you interviews with the UK's leading employers (500+ UK Health Clubs) with an average starting salary of £20K-£30K. You'll also benefit from our experience and ongoing career support once you've graduated.
- Our Corporate Partner Sponsored programme can be fully funded through our Career Loan Scheme so that you can complete your training and repay once employed and working.
- No previous experience or qualifications are necessary.

1. What is the name of this organisation?
2. Is the training offered here free? How do you know? Select the words / phrases that tell us.
3. Is there a minimum or maximum age to apply for this training?
4. What is meant by *highly motivated individuals*?
5. What does it mean by *distraction free learning*?

CARE WORKER

- Freedom Choice Care has been delivering High Quality Home Care in Cardiff for over a decade.
- Tasks include personal care, help with washing and dressing, domestic tasks, meal preparation, shopping. Previous experience preferred but not necessary as full training will be provided to NVQ level 2/3.
- Successful applicants are required to provide a new enhanced CRB disclosure; expense will be met by Freedom Choice Care. You must have a full driving licence and have your own vehicle as this is a mobile position.
- Earn £7.50 - £9.00 per hour. Guaranteed hours.
- Telephone 029 20455555. freedomchoice9@btconnect.com, www.freedomchoicecare.com

1. How long has Freedom Choice Care been in business?
2. Do you have to pay for the Criminal Record check that the job requires? How do you know?
3. Why don't they tell you where the work is based?

ADMINISTRATOR

Contract: *Permanent*
Category: *Full Time*

Job Sector: *Administration / Office Work, Hotels / Leisure*

Region: *South Wales*

Location: *Cardiff*

Salary: £12,000 to £13,000 per annum

Your main duties will include:-

- Dealing with reservations by phone, e-mail, letter, fax or face-to-face
- Checking guests into and out of the hotel, allocating rooms and handing out keys
- Preparing bills and taking payments
- Dealing with special requests from guests (e.g. storing valuables)
- Answering questions about facilities in the hotel and the surrounding area

Skills and Experience:-

- Experience within the hotel industry
- Articulate and communicative
- Numerate, computer literate
- Good interpersonal skills
- Organised and systematic
- Have a good knowledge of local area

Working Hours:
40 Hours a week, Monday – Sunday, 7am till 3pm or 3pm till 11pm.

Company Description
The Legacy Cardiff International Hotel is nestled just beneath the fairytale Castell Coch (Red Castle) in the village of Tongwynlais, just 15 minutes by car from Cardiff City Centre. Leisure and business travellers alike will find hotel amenities to suit their needs. Business guests can make use of the banquet and meeting rooms, exhibition space and the photocopying and fax services. Free Wi-Fi is available in selected public areas.

1. Why does this job require good knowledge of the area?
2. What does *articulate and communicative* mean?
3. What kind of person would NOT be suited to this job? Think about:-

   - The qualities needed
   - The hours
   - The location

Getting It Right

If you have to write a letter of application for a job, it's vital that it's the very best you can produce; if there are a large number of applications, many will be rejected at this stage because the letters are weak. They can be poor for a number of different reasons:-

- They do not give the information required
- They are badly written / punctuated
- They are set out incorrectly

Take a look at this letter of application and discuss with a partner whether you would have called the applicant for an interview or not, giving your reasons.

---

23 Lark Rise
Treetops
Downtown
L14 5RT

23/2/2012

Dear Sir,

I seen your advert in the local paper. It was about the hotel job in Cardiff so I thought id apply.

I havent done a job in a hotel before but i do catering for GCSE and get good grades. I haven't been to Cardiff before but my sister lives near there.

Im good on the computer and very chatty and like to talk to people. I don't want to work weekends though because im a dj two and i do a lot of late night gigs.

Let me know weather you want to see me for a interview. I've enclosed my VC.

Faithfully

Wayne Sprocket (Mr)

Now rewrite the letter correcting the errors.

Reading

Skim and scan the following web article then answer the questions.

Apprenticeships

If you fancy learning the trade of your choice and earning as you go, an apprenticeship might be just the thing.

What is an Apprenticeship?

- An Apprenticeship offers a practical balance between learning a trade and earning a living
- You're paid a small sum to work within a skilled environment and get the skills you need while learning with a local training provider, like a college
- It's becoming a popular career option; since 1996/7 over two million people have started an Apprenticeship and numbers of new starts are increasing every year
- The length of time it takes to complete an Apprenticeship varies; they generally last between one and three years

What are my rights as an apprentice?

- You will be paid a minimum of £95 per week, but the average salary is £170 per week and some apprentices even earn over £200 per week
- If you're aged 16-18 your Apprenticeship will be fully funded; for 19-24 year-olds your employer will be expected to contribute to your training costs
- You'll receive work benefits such as pension contributions and holiday periods; each year you will be given at least 20 days' paid holiday as well as bank holidays

What's in it for me?

You can take all kinds of apprenticeships; there are over 180 different career choices in 80 different industries, from childcare to plumbing, tourism or even design. Whatever you choose to pursue, they all lead to National Vocational Qualifications (NVQs), and Key Skills qualifications. Some apprenticeships also offer BTEC or City & Guilds certificates and some can even help you build up UCAS points to apply to university.

You can take all kinds of apprenticeships; there are over 180 different career choices in 80 different industries

Applying for an apprenticeship

Applying for an apprenticeship is very much like applying for a job; you choose where you would like to work and then apply for a place. You can apply at anytime during the year, but if you're successful, the start date for your apprenticeship will be decided by your employer. It's likely that you'll be interviewed, and you might also be asked to take some tests to make sure you're the right person for the job.

For more information on apprenticeships see the article on our sister site Lifetracks.com.

1. How long does the average apprenticeship last?
2. What is the minimum you will earn as an apprentice?
3. How much paid holiday will you receive?
4. Will you have to do any exams to become an apprentice?

Now **read more closely**.

5. How does the article try to persuade you to become an apprentice?

Think of:-

- what they tell you
- the words and phrases they use to persuade

Reading

"Would You Like A Lucrative And Enjoyable New Career As An Electrician?"

Are you sick of your current job? Would you like a new career that offers potential earnings of up to £50,747 per year? Do you want to have a job that is both rewarding and enjoyable? Becoming an electrician can offer such rewards.

"The average wage of an electrician is £37,823."

Daily Mail

Electrician's Goldmine
The regulators are likely to deliver a goldmine for qualified electricians. Like plumbers they will see their wages rocket to as much as £70,000 a year.

1. Why does this advertisement use:-

- Questions
- Newspaper headline

Reading, Speaking and Listening

If you are shortlisted for a job, you will have to attend an interview.

Read these tips.

HOW TO CLINCH THE INTERVIEW

1. **Be on time**
   Practise getting to the venue to see how long it will take. Public transport may be useless, the traffic may have been heavy, but however reasonable your excuse is, it won't affect the fact that your chances are reduced if you're late. And remember - you never get a second chance to make a first impression.
   Aim to be early - you can always find a nearby cafe/shop/pub to wait in. And if the worst comes to the worst and you are going to be late, then ring in to tell them (make sure you have contact numbers with you).

2. **Be prepared**
   Look at the employers' website and learn something about the company before you attend your interview. Feed them the opportunity to talk proudly about something positive you have found.

3. **Write down and practise possible questions**
   Writing questions and answers down and practicing them with someone will make it easier to remember when you get to the interview. And avoid sounding as though you assume the job is yours.

4. **What are your weaknesses?**
   Try to find an area of your experience/skill that is currently lacking. An interviewer will appreciate your honesty- as long as whatever you disclose can be easily remedied.

5. **You never get a second chance to make a first impression**
   SMILE! Dress professionally in simple business attire. And don't forget a firm handshake and to maintain eye contact - without glaring!

6. **Be honest**
   There's no point lying about your background and/or skills. If you get caught, you can be sure you won't be around for long! Job interviews are about matching needs - if there isn't a good match, then chances are that the job won't work out for you.

7. **Check your CV for possible gaps**
   Make sure you know how you are going to explain any time gaps on your CV.

8. **Talk about specific achievements**
   Interviewers like to know how you felt about a particular success. Some will ask for specific examples of things you've done that you're particularly proud of, how you solved problems, or how you learnt - and improved - from difficult situations.

9. **Don't talk too much**
   Communication is a two-way thing so give them a chance too.

10. **Take a spare photo & CV with you**
    Your interviewer won't be expecting it so you'll impress them. It also helps them remember you after the interview.

11. **Be enthusiastic and positive**
    Don't criticise previous employers, particularly within the industry. Focus on positive achievements and views.

12. **And finally, don't give up!**
    The harsh reality is you won't be offered every job, however perfect you think you may be for it. Usually it's because the interviewer was completely blind to the talent that stood before them. However, on the odd occasion where that's not the case, ask for feedback. It's invaluable for improving future results. Ask politely if they can give you any feedback for the future - there's a job out there for you somewhere.

1. Who is the audience for this piece of writing? How do you know?
2. List 5 things the article says you should do to PREPARE for the interview.
3. Which do you think is the best and which the worst piece of advice here? Give your reasons FULLY.

Speaking & Listening

Now imagine that a candidate is being interviewed for one of the jobs you have just read about.

Working in groups of 3 - 4, choose someone to play the candidate and the interviewers and ROLE PLAY the interview, starting at the moment when the candidate knocks on the door of the interview room.

REMEMBER!

- Ask appropriate questions - make up work experience if necessary and anything else you like to keep the role play going.
- Use appropriate language - formal, polite.

Writing

Now imagine that you have been called to an interview for a job you really want but at the last moment, a real emergency/crisis comes up and you can't go to the interview.

Write an email explaining why you can't attend.

Make up relevant details like the name of the firm, the job, the date / time, reason for not attending. Should you ask for another date?

SECTION 3: Life

Where to Live

Reading

- You have just got a job in Birmingham and need a place to live.
- You can afford £420 per month
- You have a car
- You are starting work on April 1st
- Your family will want to stay with you at some point.

In the local newspaper, there are several advertisements.

Read them carefully so that you can make a good choice.

FOR RENT

SINCLAIR COURT, PARK ROAD
Recently refurbished. Modern kitchen.
Shower, 1 available. From £350 pcm.
Next Unit Available: 6/05/11. Garages
available to tenants for £32 pcm (subject
to availability).

BURFORD COURT, GREEN COURT RD.
1 bedroom Apartments. Lounge/kitchen.
Modern block. 1 available. From £465
pcm
Next Unit Available: 1/04/11. Garages
available to tenants for £32 pcm (subject
to availability).

**SHARON COURT, DUDLEY PARK, ACOCKS
GREEN**
1 bedroom Apartments. Own garden. 1
available. From £440 pcm. Next Unit
Available: 8/04/11. Garages available to
tenants for £32 pcm (subject to
availability).

**MALFIELD COURT, 208 LEACH LANE,
REDNAL**
Studio Apartment. 1 available. From
£340pcm. Next Unit Available: 14/03/11.
Garages available to tenants for £32 pcm
(subject to availability).

**MALIN COURT, DOVEDALE ROAD, PERRY
COMMON**
1 bedroom Apartments, 1 available. No
pets or children. Three months rent in
advance.
From £450 pcm. Next Unit Available:
14/03/11. On-site parking available.

**BENTHAM COURT, BELL HOLLOWAY,
NORTHFIELD**
2 bedroom Apartments. 2 available. From
£410 pcm. Next Unit Available: 14/03/11
Garages available to tenants for £32 pcm
(subject to availability).

CHURCH ROAD, MOSEEU
1 bedroom Apartments. 1 available. From
£450 pcm. Next Unit Available: 1/04/11
Garages available to tenants for £32 pcm
(subject to availability).

**GRAYFIELD COURT, 226 LEACH LANE,
REDNAL**
1 bedroom Apartment. 1 available. From
£430 pcm. Next Unit Available: 8/04/1.
Garages available to tenants for £32 pcm
(subject to availability).

Which of the flats:-
1. has a garage?
2. won't let you keep pets?
3. has a garden?
4. needs three months rent in advance?
5. is a studio apartment – and what does this mean?
6. has been recently smartened up?

Speaking and Listening

Now with a partner, discuss which of the flats you think would be your best choice, then choose one of you to be the new tenant and the other to be the estate agent and role play the telephone conversation you might have when you ring up to say you would like to take the flat.

REMEMBER!
You will both be quite formal - this is a business deal.
Think of the kind of questions you might ask:-
Tenant
• Is the flat still available?
• Is there a deposit to pay?
• When could you move in?
• Are there any restrictions - things you can't do or have as a tenant?

Agent
• Do you have references?
• How old are you? Will you be living there alone?
• Are you employed? Where?
• Do you have a bank account?

You could end with making an appointment for you to come in to the office to sign a tenancy agreement.

Leisure Time

Reading

**Take a look at this example which shows how to book tickets for The London Eye.
Now skim to find out:-**

• WHEN you can go on it
• If you can save by going with a group

Combination Tickets

Combine your experience with other attractions!
Combine your experience at the London Eye with a London Eye River Cruise or visits to other attractions for a great day out and big savings on tickets!
Book now and save up to 33%

20% off Group Standard Tickets

Spring special offer for groups!
Take 20% off Group Standard Tickets and Group Sunset and Night Experiences in March and April to celebrate the arrival of spring.

Private Capsule

Experience breathtaking views from the luxury of your own Private Capsule with up to 25 guests.

Eye Love Mum

Take to the skies with the EDF Energy London Eye this Mother's Day!
Why not spoil your mum with a glamorous trip on the London Eye.

Chocolate Tasting Experience

Enjoy a breathtaking hour on the EDF Energy London Eye and learn about one of the world's most desired delicacies from cocoa bean to chocolate bar.

Fast Track

Benefit from priority boarding and arrive just 15 minutes before your rotation with a Fast Track Ticket to the London Eye.
Book now and save 10%

Visitor Information

Plan your trip to the London Eye, find out about our opening times, directions and details of our facilities here.

Opening times:-
January - March
daily 10.00am - 8.30pm
April to June
daily 10.00am - 9.00pm
July and August
daily 10.00am - 9.30pm
September to December
daily 10.00am - 8.30pm

Now look at the following review.

We only went on the Eye as we had got a '2 for 1' ticket, otherwise we wouldn't have paid for the 2 of us to go on it. We went early as we had heard how busy it gets. We went on a Sunday morning and it was fairly busy.... not too long to wait though. Waited for a longer time to purchase the ticket. Enjoyed the ride itself. About 16 of us in each pod so we all managed to get a good view of London. The weather was fantastic so could see for a long way. Would I go again.... maybe not. Once done, it's not something you would do again.

Date of visit: April 2011

1. What 2 negative points about this experience does the writer make?
2. Why would he not go again?

This is one of those London attractions you're better off seeing in the off season, which is exactly what we did in March 2011. There was only a few minutes wait. You can buy passes on line by searching London Eye. Even though we've visited London three other times before, the London Eye escaped us during those visits. If you only have one trip to London, don't miss it!

We loved the 4D movie before the ride and the County Hall at night with changing colours was beautiful. We recommend going around sunset to be able to get spectacular views of the Houses of Parliament and then see the changing colours.

Date of visit: March 2011

3. How do we know that this reviewer is much more enthusiastic about the experience? Look closely at the choice of words and punctuation.

Shopping

Reading

Look at this newspaper headline from October 2010.

> # What sells 1.5bn bananas a year, employs 472,000 people, flogs the UK's cheapest engagement ring and makes £6,000 a minute? Our guide to Tesco by numbers.

1. Why do newspaper headlines often use QUESTIONS and STATISTICS?

Tesco's website has this advice for online grocery shoppers.

- **Stick to your budget**
  A running total is shown as you shop, so you won't get a nasty surprise at the checkout.
- **Only buy what you need**
  By avoiding impulse buys and with no pester power, you'll find online shopping is a great way to keep to your list.
- **Cheaper Alternatives**
  We have over 6000 'Cheaper Alternatives' on top selling brands so you can easily switch and save.
- **All offers in one place**
  Over 1,000 of them each week, all grouped together so they are easy to find.
- **Save on fuel**
  We'll deliver groceries to your door.
- **Collect Clubcard Points**
  Just like in-store, plus you can spend them online too.

Why might these tips be useful to:-

- A mother with young children
- A pensioner with no car

The following is an article about opposition to the building of a new Tesco store. Read it and answer the questions.

Tesco defends store from potential threat

SECURITY is tight at the site of a new Tesco supermarket due to open in Cheltenham Road Bristol in a matter of weeks.

Ten security guards are thought to staff the building 24 hours, seven days week to ensure the controversial new supermarket is not damaged or inhabited by squatters.

There are concerns about the security of the store, particularly when it first opens, as protesters who have attended council meetings have already threatened direct action.

It is thought the shop will open in the next week or so, but Tesco does not want to reveal the exact date.

The supermarket giant has faced strong opposition since it first announced its plan to open.

Tesco says it wants to boost an area that has a number of empty shops and will create up to 20 new jobs but some residents feel a large corporation is wrong for the area. Meanwhile some traders fear it will have a negative effect on their businesses.

Ahmed Ahrad, 52, owner of Cafe Sufi in Stokes Croft, believes Tesco will be bad for business.

"When a supermarket moves into an area it ruins the smaller shops that are already struggling with high business rates," he said.

However, Geoff Gardiner, owner of Fred Baker Cycles based next door to the new Tesco, said he thought it might encourage more new businesses into derelict buildings.

"I'm simply in favour of the road having commerce," he said. "Other businesses will just have to up their game."

A Tesco spokeswoman said: "We are looking forward to welcoming our first customers to the store in Cheltenham Road when we open later this month.

"We've always said that we are proud to be investing in the area, creating new jobs and providing choice and competition."

1. Which city is this store opening in?
2. How many jobs will it create?
3. Which shop that is already there will be next to the new Tesco?
4. How does its owner feel about having Tesco as a neighbour?
5. Why do local traders generally not welcome the new store?
6. Why does the article **quote** the words of Ahmed Ahrad and the Tesco spokeswoman?

Speaking and Listening

People who have businesses close to this new Tesco might well not want any competition but what about those who live nearby?

Imagine you are:-

1. **Jim, a pensioner who is not very mobile.**
2. **Lisa, a mother of three children under five who has no car.**
3. **Rory, single, who works shifts.**

Say what their opinions might be and the reasons why.

Reading

Many people buy and sell on EBay. Read the following advice on Selling and answer the questions that follow.

Research your item and the rules of selling

Do some research, especially about setting a starting price, listing format, and category. This will help you create a good listing and get the best price for your item. Compare your item with active and completed listings on eBay based on category, format, and selling price. Selecting a category explains how to search for and select a category. Selecting a selling format tells you more about format choices.

Buyers feel more compelled to bid and buy when they know the postage costs beforehand. Package, weigh, and measure your item so you can use calculated postage. If this is your first time selling an item, you may be required to specify postage. Calculating postage costs tells you how to do this. Visit the eBay Postage Centre to learn more about posting your items.

Learn about eBay policies on prohibited and restricted items, as well as what items are accepted or prohibited when listing and completing the sale at 'Knowing the rules for sellers'.

1. What do you understand by CATEGORY of item?
2. Put the following into categories:-
   - Women's sandals
   - The book *Black Beauty*
   - A car
   - A necklace
   - A food processor
3. Why according to this web article do buyers feel happier to bid for an item which states how much the postage is?
4. How does eBay help you calculate the postage?
5. What is a *prohibited or restricted* item?

Writing

This is an advertisement that appeared on eBay for an item.

It should have been proofread more carefully. Correct it and rewrite a more helpful advertisement.

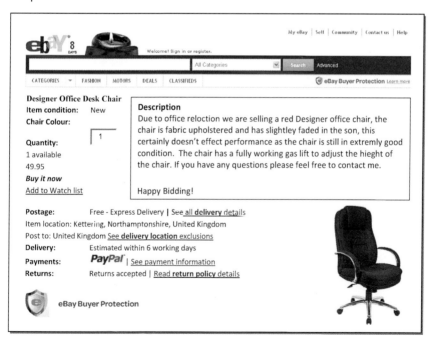

Technology

Reading

IM - free HTC Sensation priced and dated

12 May 2011

Play.com says £499.99 from 30 June

Vodafone has an exclusive on the contract version, that we already know. But what if you don't want to be tied to a Vodafone contract for the next 18 months? Well, you could wait for the other networks to offer one, which should be around a month or so later - or you could go down the SIM-free route. It still might mean a wait though.

Vodafone does indeed have an exclusive and so far, none of the usual SIM-free suspects have come forward with a price, but Play.com has now come forward with its own offer. According to TechRadar, the price of a SIM-free Sensation is £499.99, with 30 June being the provisional date of shipping.

The Sensation certainly looks like a phone to have, with Android 2.3.3, HTC Sense 3.0, a 1.2GHz dual-core Qualcomm Snapdragon processor, 768MB of RAM, an eight-megapixel camera with 1080p video recording and a 4.2-inch SLCD screen with a qHD display. Get the full breakdown here or check out our hands-on here.

1. How much is the HTC Sensation going to cost?
2. When will it be available to buy?
3. Where can you buy it?
4. What does *SIM free* mean?
5. What does the *provisional date for shipping* mean?
6. Which network offers this phone on contract?
7. What does *exclusive* mean?
8. Name one advantage and one disadvantage of having your mobile on a contract.
9. Look at the technical details in the last paragraph. Do you think many people will understand or care about these? Why do advertisements often give us these technical details?

Now read the following review of a phone and answer the questions on it.

Sonim Force Review ★ ★ ★ ★ ☆

03 May 2011 | Avg. **user rating:** ✓ ✓ ✓ ✓ ✓

Look and feel
A brick of a phone, the Sonim Force certainly feels as though it can take a beating, aided by a rubber casing that absorbs any shocks and knocks

Ease of use
The lack of features makes the Sonim Force a breeze to get to grips with. The keys are raised and well positioned to enable a relatively speedy typing process

Features
Though not designed as a feature phone the inclusion of GPS is a welcome addition for a phone built for the outdoors, as is a music player, two-megapixel camera and Opera Mini web browser

Performance
The Sonim Force survived all we threw, hit or drowned it with. If you're after a true tough-phone then this is a phone that delivers

Battery life
A phenomenal talktime of 1,080 minutes and 800 hours standby is just what you want from a phone built for the outdoors

Sonim Force
Pros: It withstood all we threw and dropped on it, proving it's very much water, shock, dust and drop proof
Cons: A brute of a phone, the Sonim Force is heavy and cumbersome

Look and Feel	★ ☆ ☆ ☆
Ease of use	★ ★ ★ ★ ☆
Features	★ ☆ ☆ ☆
Performance	★ ★ ★ ★ ★
Battery life	★ ★ ★ ★ ★

Mobile Choice Total Score

★ ★ ★ ★ ☆

Verdict: In terms of the number of knocks the Sonim XP3300 Force can endure, no phone comes close. This is the daddy of tough-phones.

1.   Why has this review used subheadings?
2.   Who might be the ideal user for this phone? Quote 2 words / phrases to prove your point.
3.   What do the expressions PROS and CONs mean in this review?
4.   Look at the words and phrases that persuade:-

   - *It can take a beating*
   - *GPS is a welcome addition*
   - *A phone that delivers*
   - *Phenomenal talktime*
   - *The daddy of tough phones*

Writing

Write a review of your own mobile phone using the subheadings in this review.

Reading

Some schools ban the use of mobile phones - perhaps yours is one.

The first article comes from the Internet.

Mobile phones would be outlawed in UK classrooms under Conservative Party plans to beef up discipline in schools.

The Tories said in an education policy document that they wanted to see authority returned to teachers. They reckoned an important part of that proposal would include a crackdown on the use of mobile phones.

a)   Why do the Tories want *a crackdown on the use of mobile phones?*

This is an extract from a secondary school's policy document on the subject of mobile phones.

Our mobile phone policy aims to deal with these problems in school *by banning the use of mobile phones during the school day without the explicit approval of a member of staff.* If they are brought into school they should be switched off or on silent mode and kept out of sight. We are not preventing students from carrying mobile phones but wish them to be used sensibly and with consideration.

b)   What is this school's policy on phones in your own words?
c)   In your experience do you think this policy works?

Speaking and Listening

Imagine that your school has a strict 'no mobiles' policy and you have been chosen from your year to argue the case for limited use of mobile phones to the Head and governors. Write your speech.

REMEMBER!
- This is a formal situation so choose appropriate language and tone.
- Show that you understand some of the problems that mobile phones present to the smooth running of a school.
- Give some practical reasons why you think pupils should be able to access their phones and any benefits they may get from doing so.
- Be reasonable, not critical or sarcastic.
- End appropriately.

One of the reasons that schools dislike pupils having mobiles in school is that there are often thefts.

Look at the following incident.

In Anytown Academy 11TY were having an English lesson with Mr Henderson when a mobile phone went off. The school has a 'no mobile' rule. The class were doing a controlled assessment and the teacher was extremely annoyed as this disturbed pupils' concentration. He took the phone from Louis Havers and put it on the teacher's desk. The class continued to work. Mr Henderson forgot about the phone and dismissed the class but when Louis came up to him at the end of the lesson and asked for his phone back, Mr Henderson said it would be confiscated until the end of the week. He then found that the phone had disappeared from his desk.

Louis's parents made an appointment to come to school to see the Head.

Write Mr Henderson's report of the incident.

REMEMBER!
- Dates and times
- Order of events
- Factual detail – don't become too emotionally involved
- End appropriately

Getting It Right

Many 'spelling mistakes' are made by writing the wrong word which sounds the same as the correct one - HERE instead of HEAR for instance. These words are called **homophones.** Look at some of the most commonly confused words.

THERE - a place where	• **e.g.** Put it down *there*
part of **there is / are**	• **e.g.** *There* is no reason to go
THEY'RE - short for **there are**	• **e.g.** *They're* always late
THEIR - belonging to them	• **e.g.** *Their* train was delayed
TO - towards	• **e.g.** She went *to* town
In front of an infinitive	• **e.g.** He wanted *to* swim
TOO - also	• **e.g.** Charlie was invited *too*
an excess of	• **e.g.** The coffee was *too* hot
TWO - a number, 2	• **e.g.** I waited *two* hours
WEAR - to have clothes on	• **e.g.** What shall I *wear*?
WHERE - position, location	• **e.g.** *Where* did I put it?
WERE - part of verb to be	• **e.g.** *Were* you at Jo's party?
IT'S belonging to it	• **e.g.** The puppy hurts *its* paw
IT'S short for it is	• **e.g.** *It's* ages since I saw you
KNOW - to have knowledge of	• **e.g.** I *know* your family well
NO - opposite of yes, a negative	• **e.g.** I've got *no* time for him

| **KNEW** - past tense of know | • **e.g.** I *knew* your family well |
| **NEW** - opposite of old | • **e.g.** She's got *new* shoes |

| **PASSED** - moved by | • **e.g.** I *passed* him in the street |
| succeeded | • **e.g.** I *passed* French last year |

| **PAST** - preposition beyond, by | • **e.g.** She rushed *past* me |
| time gone by | • **e.g.** That's all in *the past* |

| **QUIET -** opposite of loud | • **e.g.** It was a *quiet* street |
| **QUITE -** rather, somewhat | • **e.g.** She's *quite* pretty |

Now proofread this piece of writing carefully. There are other homophones here as well.

Saima new that her new friend wood be a grate girl to hang out with at the weekends. They shared the same tastes in music, in close and in films. In the passed Saima had had friends who where quiet quite, too shy too have a laugh or do exciting things with. Butt Zara was different. Although she was bright and clever in school, she didn't knead to bee always talking about her successes and their was nothing boastful about her. When she and Saima met up after lessons, they're first thoughts wear too go of into town and walk around the shops, have a milk sheik, then go back home and do sum homework.

After French wear they were in different setts, they were to meat up outside the gaits. Saima weighted ten minutes then texted her friend but they're was know reply. Puzzled, Saima walked back into school and sore to her surprise Zara deep in conversation with a boy she did not know. He was shaking Zara's arm and looked quite angry. She seamed too be clothes two tears. Saima watched them fore a minute then slowly walked of. Their was much about this knew friend she did not now.